Contents

C000079187

The Diary of a Killer Cat

The Diary of a Killer Cat is the first book in the *Killer Cat* series written by Anne Fine. The diary is written from the point of view of a pet cat called Tuffy, who always seems to get on the wrong side of his owners. In this extract, Tuffy is in their bad books for killing a bird.

1: Monday

OKAY, OKAY. So hang me. I killed the bird. For pity's sake, I'm a *cat*. It's practically my *job* to go creeping round the garden after sweet little eensy-weensy birdy-pies that can hardly fly from one hedge to another. So what am I supposed to do when one of the poor feathery little flutterballs

5 just about throws itself into my mouth? I mean, it practically landed on my paws. It could have *hurt* me.

Okay, *okay*. So I biffed it. Is that any reason for Ellie to cry in my fur so hard I almost *drown*, and squeeze me so hard I almost *choke*?

"Oh, Tuffy!" she says, all sniffles and red eyes and piles of wet tissues. "Oh, Tuffy. How could you

10 *do* that?"

How could I *do* that? I'm a *cat*. How did I know there was going to be such a giant great fuss, with Ellie's mother rushing off to fetch sheets of old newspaper, and Ellie's father filling a bucket with soapy water?

Okay, *okay*. So maybe I shouldn't have dragged it in and left it on the carpet. And maybe the

15 stains won't come out, ever.

So *hang* me.

2: Tuesday

I quite enjoyed the little funeral. I don't think they really wanted me to come, but, after all, it's just as much my garden as theirs. In fact, I spend a whole lot more time in it than they do. I'm the

20 only one in the family who uses it properly.

Not that they're grateful. You ought to hear them.

"That cat is *ruining* my flower beds. There are hardly any of the petunias left."

"I'd barely *planted* the lobelias before it was lying on top of them, squashing them flat."

"I *do* wish it wouldn't dig holes in the anemones."

25 Moan, moan, moan, moan. I don't know why they bother to keep a cat, since all they ever seem to do is complain.

An extract from *The Diary of a Killer Cat* by Anne Fine.

1 Give one feature of the text that shows it's a diary.

....

1 mark

2 How does Ellie feel about Tuffy killing the bird? How can you tell?

....

....

2 marks

3 Why do you think Ellie's father was filling a bucket of water (lines 12-13)?

....

....

1 mark

4 What did the family do the day after Tuffy killed the bird?

....

1 mark

5 Why do you think the author repeats the word "moan" on line 25?

....

....

1 mark

6 The author has put some of the words in italics. Why do you think she has done this?

....

....

2 marks

7 Do you think that Tuffy was wrong to kill the bird? Explain your answer.

....

2 marks

....

....

Total
out of 10

Geocaching

This article explores 'geocaching' — a hi-tech treasure hunt where people are given GPS* coordinates as clues. These coordinates tell them the location of a hidden item, which is usually outdoors. Geocaching has become popular in many different countries across the world.

Challenge yourself with a GPS-assisted treasure hunt

Geocaching is sending the nation's tech-savvy pirates into a frenzy. A great family activity, you can join in the fun by tracking down hidden booty near you.

5 A family treasure hunt is fantastic fun, especially if you have a garden, but geocaching adds a genuine sense of mystery and adventure because you never know what you'll find or where it will be.

10 Geocaching is an increasingly popular treasure-hunting game in which participants use GPS-enabled devices to navigate their way to a specific set of GPS coordinates and then attempt to find the geocache
15 (container) hidden at that location. There are very likely to be caches hidden around your local area. To get going, simply download the free app at geocaching.com and search for caches near you.

20 Caches come in all shapes and sizes. It could be a tin hanging from a branch or a tupperware box in a tree cavity — you need to be sharp-eyed once you get close. Inside the cache you'll find some little goodies —
25 a toy soldier, a cheap pendant, or maybe a

Geocaching is a worldwide treasure hunt game that anyone can join.

logbook. Sign the book and trade the toy with another goodie or add to the cache. Alternatively, make your own cache and hide it somewhere clever near you and then
30 post its location on the geocaching website.

The beauty of this game is that you never know what you'll find or where. It's active, it teaches map skills and it encourages children to explore their local countryside
35 — although with nearly two million caches worldwide you can enjoy the game pretty much anywhere.

From *www.telegraph.co.uk*

Glossary

GPS (Global Positioning System) — a navigation system where signals from satellites are used to show the exact location of something. Devices able to receive GPS signals include mobile phones and sat navs.

1 Why do you think the author uses the word "pirates" (line 2) to describe people who look for geocaches?

....

....

2 marks

2 Find and copy one word from lines 8-9 which makes geocaching sound exciting.

....

1 mark

3 Give two examples of items you might find hidden inside a cache.

....

1 mark

4 How do you think the author feels about geocaching? Explain your answer.

....

....

2 marks

5 How does the layout of the text show you that it is a newspaper article?

....

....

2 marks

6 Give one possible disadvantage of geocaching. Explain your answer.

....

2 marks

....

Total
out of 10

....

The Dragonsitter's Island

The Dragonsitter's Island is told through a set of emails between a boy called Eddie and his uncle, Morton. Eddie is looking after Morton's pet dragons while Morton goes on holiday. However, strange things start happening while Morton's away and Eddie thinks he knows why...

From: Morton Pickle
To: Edward Smith-Pickle
Date: Friday 24 February
Subject: Re: Nessie

5   Dear Eddie

Please don't be offended if I say this, but I really don't think you have seen the Loch Ness Monster.

A few years ago, I made a study of the myths and legends surrounding that fabulous beast. I wondered whether it might be a dragon, or a distant relative of the dragon which had somehow become aquatic*.

Sadly I discovered that there is no reliable evidence that the monster has ever existed. All the sightings
10 are, I'm afraid to say, the work of drunks, maniacs*, frauds*, fantasists* and publicity-seekers of one sort or another.

I wish the monster did exist, but it doesn't. And even if it did, it would be swimming around Loch Ness, not my island.

In the years that I've been living there, I have spotted whales, dolphins, seals and even the occasional
15 otter, so you may have been lucky enough to see one of them.

I don't know who or what has been stealing Mr McDougall's sheep but I can tell you one thing for certain: it is not Nessie.

Morton

From: Edward Smith-Pickle
20 To: Morton Pickle
Date: Friday 24 February
Subject: Re: Re: Nessie
Attachments: Evidence

If the monster doesn't exist, what's this?

25 Eddie

Glossary

aquatic — able to live in water

maniac — someone who has an unhealthy obsession with something

fraud — someone who tricks other people

fantasist — someone who thinks imaginary things are real

From: Morton Pickle
To: Edward Smith-Pickle
Date: Friday 24 February
Subject: Re: Re: Re: Nessie

30 I'm coming home! Will change my tickets and catch next plane!

Do not approach the monster till I get there! It might be dangerous!

M

An extract from
The Dragonsitter's Island
by Josh Lacey.

1 How does the text's layout show you that Eddie and Morton are writing emails to each other?

....

....

2 marks

2 Explain what "reliable evidence" (line 9) is.

....

1 mark

3 Why do you think people might pretend to have seen the Loch Ness Monster?

....

1 mark

4 What has happened on the island to make Eddie worry that something is wrong?

....

1 mark

5 How does the author change his writing style in lines 30-32 to show that Morton is excited?

....

....

2 marks

6 Why do you think Morton wants to come home when he realises that Eddie has seen the Loch Ness Monster?

....

....

1 mark

7 How would you react if someone told you they had seen a monster?

....

....

....

2 marks

Total
out of 10

GRRRR

Francesca Beard is a Malaysian writer based in London. She is also a spoken word poet — this means her poems are written to be performed out loud to an audience. Francesca's poems often include a lot of repetition and strong rhyme schemes. *GRRRR* is one of these poems.

If you smile then I will glare,

If you're sad then I don't care,

If you tell me I've been bad, I will say 'Oh
   good, I'm glad!'

5 *I don't want to, I don't like you!*

If you touch me, I will bite you!

If you try to calm me down, I will roll round
   on the ground.

If you try to make me stop, I will scream until

10 I pop.

If you shh me, I will yell and yeLL and yELL
   and YELL and YELL!

I don't want to, I don't like you!

If you touch me, I will bite you!

15 If you try to make me eat, I'll spit my food out
   on the floor,

If you try to make me sleep, I'll bang my head
   against the door.

If you sing a lullaby, I'll join in the key* of Y!

20 *I don't want to, I don't like you!*

If you touch me, I will bite you!

I'm the worst there's ever been, I'm the worst
   you've ever seen,

I'm a single-handed RIOT!!!!!!!!!!!!!!!!!!!!!!!!!!!!!!!!!!

25 !!!!!!!!!!!!!!!!!!!!!!!!!!!!!!!!!

(Now I'm ready to be quiet)

Francesca Beard

Glossary

key — the pitch a piece of music is written in

1 Why do you think the poet chose the title "GRRRR"?

....
1 mark

2 Find two pairs of words that rhyme in lines 1-4.

....
2 marks

3 The word "yell" is written in four different ways on lines 11 and 12. Why do you think the poet chose to do this?

....

....
1 mark

4 Why do you think there are so many exclamation marks after the word "riot" (line 24)?

....

....
1 mark

5 Why do you think the poet put the last line of the poem in brackets?

....

....
1 mark

6 Who do you think is talking in the poem? How can you tell?

....

....
2 marks

7 Would you like to meet the narrator? Explain your answer.

....
2 marks

....

Total
out of 10

....

Julius Caesar's Goat

Julius Caesar was born in Ancient Rome in 100BC. He was a talented army general and soon became very powerful. Eventually, he became the ruler of Rome. Julius Caesar is the main character in *Julius Caesar's Goat* by Dick King-Smith, which tells a fictional version of his life.

Chapter Two

Now, as his legions* prepared to march south to confront the army of Pompey, Caesar issued an order with regard to his new pet. Caesar's goat was to be given all possible honour, and anyone found guilty of treating it with disrespect would be put to death.

5 As for the man who would have executed the animal if the general's thumb had turned down, he, much to his dismay, was appointed Centurion-Capricorn*. Not even a rise in pay of one *denarius per diem* (a penny a day) could compensate* him for having now to live permanently next to that awful

10 pong, but of course he could not complain.

'*Caseus durus!*' his mates whispered to him (which, loosely translated, means 'Hard cheese!').

Now, as the legions moved south, Julius Caesar and his bodyguard, along with the Centurion-Capricorn and the animal itself, marched in the middle of the column of

15 soldiers.

At first the wind was in the south and thus blew in their faces.

It was a strong wind, so all those marching in front of Caesar were in luck, for they were spared the smell of the billy goat. All those behind Caesar, however, caught the full impact of the wind-borne stink.

20 They struggled along, holding their noses and trying not to breathe in. Luckily for them, however, the wind soon changed. Now it was blowing steadily from the north and it was the turn of the soldiers marching in front of Caesar to cough and splutter at the awful smell. It blew from the north all the rest of the day, by which time the soldiers at the front were absolutely fed up. But no one dared say a word to Caesar.

An extract from *Julius Caesar's Goat* by Dick King-Smith.

Glossary

legions — large groups of Roman soldiers   Centurion-Capricorn — officer in charge of the goat

compensate — make up for something

1 Why don't the soldiers like Julius Caesar's goat?

....
1 mark

2 Read lines 5-7. What do you think might have happened in Chapter One of this book?

....

....
1 mark

3 How do you think the man who is made Centurion-Capricorn feels about his new job? Explain your answer.

....

....
2 marks

4 What do the soldiers mean when they say "Hard cheese!" (line 12)?

....
1 mark

5 Find and copy two words from the extract that mean 'smell'.

....
1 mark

6 Explain why nobody complained to Julius Caesar about his goat.

....

....
2 marks

7 Do you think that this is a very serious story? Explain your answer.

....
2 marks

Total
out of 10

Armoured Dinosaurs

Even though dinosaurs became extinct around 65 million years ago, scientists are still uncovering new facts about them. Some dinosaurs had their own body armour to protect them from attacks. This extract looks at the different types of body armour and why they were so effective.

Armoured Dinosaurs

When we think about dinosaurs, we often imagine them with snarling teeth and vicious claws, but that wasn't always the case. For some dinosaurs, being able to protect themselves was far more important than being good at attacking others.

One of the most effective forms of protection was body armour. Some dinosaurs
5   developed protective plates, horns, spikes or clubs on the outside of their bodies to defend themselves against predators. Even if the appearance of this armour wasn't enough to put off an attacker, trying to fight through jagged spikes wasn't a task for the faint-hearted.

Dino Defence

Some of the best-known armoured dinosaurs are the Ankylosaurus and the Stegosaurus.

10 **Ankylosauruses** had a layer of strong, bony scales called scutes, which covered their head, shoulders and back. These scutes were made of bone and covered with keratin — the same material found in our fingernails and toenails. This made the scutes very difficult to break. Lethal spikes ran in rows down the dinosaur's back and tail, which had a large rectangular club at the end. This meant that Ankylosauruses weren't just hard to attack — they stood a
15 pretty good chance of hurting anything that had a go!

Stegosauruses had two rows of large diamond-shaped plates that ran the length of their back and down part of their tail. These plates stuck out at an angle on either side of their spine, which intimidated predators looking to launch an attack. If that didn't work, the four savage spikes sticking out of the end of their tail were a good way of fending off any
20 pluckier predators.

Both of these dinosaurs could grow to be the length of a bus. This, coupled with the weight of their armour, meant that they found it difficult to run away quickly. They often had to stand their ground and fight.

Some animals still have body armour...

25 Dinosaurs may no longer roam the Earth, but body armour is still around today. Animals like turtles, armadillos, crocodiles and hedgehogs all have their own armour to repel predators.

This is what an Ankylosaurus may have looked like.

Written by Louise McEvoy.

1 Why do you think fighting a dinosaur with body armour "wasn't a task for the faint-hearted" (line 7)?

....
....
1 mark

2 Why has the author put the words "Ankylosauruses" (line 10) and "Stegosauruses" (line 16) in bold?

....
....
1 mark

3 Read lines 10-20. Give two ways that the body armour of an Ankylosaurus and the body armour of a Stegosaurus were similar.

....
....
2 marks

4 What does the word "intimidated" (line 18) mean? Use a dictionary to help you.

....
1 mark

5 According to the text, why couldn't Stegosauruses run quickly? Circle one.

a. Because they had short legs.　　b. Because they were very heavy.
c. Because their body plates got in the way.　　d. Because they were very tall.

1 mark

6 Is this a fiction or a non-fiction text? Explain your answer.

....
....
2 marks

7 Do you think that the layout of this text is helpful? Explain your answer.

....
2 marks

....

Total
out of 10

....

The Story of Nu Wa

The Story of Nu Wa is a Chinese myth that is hundreds of years old. It tells the story of a goddess called Nu Wa who saved the Earth from destruction. Because the myth is so old, there are many different versions of it. One of the most popular versions is described below.

Contrary to popular belief, not all gods are perfect — they have flaws just like you and me. Some gods are vengeful, some are cruel, some are vain and some are unbearably arrogant. But no gods were more arrogant than two gods who lived many, many moons ago: Gong Gong, the God of Water, and Zhu Rong,
5   the God of Fire. These two quarrelsome gods each thought they were more powerful than the other.

"I am superior!" crowed Gong Gong. "Look how much devastation I can cause by flooding the plains!" And with a nod of his head the river below him burst its banks and washed into the surrounding farmland.

10 "Water is no match for fire!" spat Zhu Rong, as he sent a jet of flame to Earth and reduced a forest to cinders.

The fight between the two gods raged on and on, and they brought untold misery to humankind. Eventually, Gong Gong realised that he was losing the battle. Angered, he punched Mount Buzhou, an enormous mountain whose
15 summit* held up the sky. As he landed his blow, the summit collapsed, the sky caved in and the Earth cracked open. This caused the slumbering dragons that lived beneath the surface of the Earth to awaken and crawl out of the cracks. They flew out of the ground and hungrily went in search of food, breathing jets of fire as they swooped across the shattered sky.

20 A goddess called Nu Wa, who was as caring as the other gods were selfish, was distraught at the sight of the devastation and suffering. She believed that gods and goddesses should use their powers for good and decided to save humankind.

Firstly, she knew she needed to mend the sky. She melted together five coloured stones and used the mixture to repair the cracks. Next, she killed
25 a giant turtle and used its legs as pillars to support the fallen sky. Finally, she turned her attention to the dragons which were terrorising the land below. Using her bare hands, she plucked one dragon from the sky as if it were nothing but a feather and crushed it between finger and thumb, causing all the other dragons to flee in panic.

30 And this is how Nu Wa saved humankind from the selfishness of gods.

Written by Holly Robinson.

Glossary
summit — the very top of a mountain

1   **Which of the following words is closest in meaning to "flaws" (line 1)? Circle one.**

   a. problems   b. weaknesses   c. strengths   d. feelings

1 mark

2   **Which word is used instead of 'said' in line 7?
Why do you think the author chose this word?**

....

....

2 marks

3   **In your own words, explain why Mount Buzhou is important.**

....

....

1 mark

4   **Give two features of the text that suggest it is a myth.**

....

....

2 marks

5   **Do you think that Nu Wa is a powerful character? Explain your answer.**

....

....

2 marks

6   **Do Gong Gong and Zhu Rong behave like you would expect gods to act?
Explain your answer.**

....

2 marks

....

Total
out of 10

....

Coram Boy

Coram Boy is a novel by Jamila Gavin, which was turned into a play. It tells the story of two orphan boys, Toby and Aaron, who were raised at a children's home in London called Coram Hospital. In this scene, Toby and Aaron have been called to see the Matron, Mrs Hendry.

	MRS HENDRY:	Aaron. Toby. Do you know why you are here?
	TOBY:	Is it because of the mud pie?
	MRS HENDRY:	No. No it isn't. Though you can tell me about that later if you would like.
	TOBY:	No thanks, Ma'am.
5	MRS HENDRY:	Boys, I have asked you here to tell you that your time with us is at an end. On Friday you will both be leaving to begin new lives. Toby, you will go to join the household of your benefactor*, Mr Gaddarn, as a liveried* servant. You will be housed and fed. You will be allowed to attend church on Sundays and have one day off a year. Mr Gaddarn is a good and important man. [...] I trust you will serve him well.
10	TOBY:	Yes, Ma'am.
	MRS HENDRY:	Aaron. You are not yet eight and normally a little young to be apprenticed out. But Mr Handel believes you have superior talents in music. We have spoken with Mr Dangerfield and he has kindly agreed that you may now be apprenticed to a musician named Mr Brook, a protegee* of Mr Handel. You will be instructed in the art of music copying and you will also be given musical tuition.
15		
	AARON:	Music! I really want to do music!
	MRS HENDRY:	Now, as you are probably aware, it is our practice when a boy leaves to give him back any token which he came here with. Many of you had mothers who loved you very dearly and wished you to have something to remember them by.
20		*(She picks up a colourful string of beads from a tray on her desk.)*
		Toby, this string of beads was around your neck when you were brought here.
		(TOBY takes it. He is amazed and overwhelmed. His mother must have held this, touched it.)
	TOBY:	Do you know where my mother is?
25	MRS HENDRY:	No, I'm afraid I don't. The stranger who brought you here said he found you in Bristol. It is most likely that your mother was a slave, en route to the Indies.
	TOBY:	But she's a princess. And she's free now.
		(MRS HENDRY only smiles.)

An abridged extract from the play *Coram Boy*, by Helen Edmundson, based on the novel by Jamila Gavin.

Glossary

benefactor — someone who gives money to help someone else	**liveried** — in uniform	**protegee** — someone taught by somebody famous

1 Give two features of the text that show it is a playscript.

....

....

2 marks

2 How do you think Toby feels in line 2? Explain your answer.

....

....

2 marks

3 Why do you think Toby is "overwhelmed" by the string of beads in lines 22-23?

....

....

2 marks

4 Why do you think Mrs Hendy "only smiles" at Toby in line 28?

....

....

2 marks

5 How do you think Toby might feel about becoming a servant? Explain your answer.

....

2 marks

....

Total
out of 10

....

An Interview with Tim Peake

Tim Peake is a British astronaut with the European Space Agency (ESA). Between December 2015 and June 2016 he lived on the International Space Station, where he carried out important scientific experiments. He gave this interview shortly before he went into space.

What are you most nervous and excited about?

I wouldn't say I was nervous, but I'm sure there will be a moment of apprehension* when I'm sat on top of a rocket and it's about to launch. Also there's spacewalking — most astronauts say the first time the hatch opens and you go out and find yourself looking at Earth 400km beneath
5 you, it's a shock. But the spacewalk, if I get to do one, is what I'm most looking forward to. It would be wonderful if I got the opportunity.

What do you do in a typical day?

There's no such thing as a typical day! Sleeping can be quite hard because there is no day or night like on Earth — we see 16 sunrises and sunsets every day. In fact, there are new adjustable
10 lights to try to help our bodies settle into a circadian* rhythm. Every morning we're told what we will be doing by mission control and they guide us at all times. We do have short rest times, though. We can watch TV (I like to watch rugby), and there's a guitar. I play it very badly. I know a few Oasis and Coldplay songs.

What skills do you need?

15 You need to be good at team work and communicating, as astronauts are only a very small part of the huge international team that works 24/7 to support the ISS*. You also need to be calm under pressure, and generally fit and healthy. An interest in science is crucial as you need to have a good understanding of the experiments you do, and you need to work in lab conditions and use scientific equipment.

20 **What advice would you give to someone considering a career in space?**

Find out what it is that really excites you. This will no doubt also be the subject that you are best at! For me, it was an early passion for flying that led to a career as a military pilot, prior to* becoming a test pilot and gaining a degree in flight dynamics later in life. [...] If you have set your heart on something you want to do, keep going, work hard, and persevere* and
25 your dreams will come true.

An abridged extract from *www.destinationspace.uk*

Glossary

apprehension — worry   circadian — 24 hour   ISS — International Space Station

prior to — before   persevere — don't give up

(1) **What is Tim most excited about?**

....
☐ 1 mark

(2) **Explain why sleeping on the International Space Station is difficult.**

....

....
☐ 1 mark

(3) **Why do you think astronauts need to be "calm under pressure" (lines 16-17)?**

....

....
☐ 2 marks

(4) **What do you think the word "crucial" (line 17) means? Use a dictionary to help you.**

....
☐ 1 mark

(5) **How does the layout of this extract make it easier to read?**

....

....
☐ 1 mark

(6) **Do you think that life on the International Space Station sounds similar or different to life on Earth? Explain your answer.**

....

....
☐ 2 marks

(7) **Would you like to go to space? Explain your answer.**

....

....
☐ 2 marks

Total
out of 10
☐

Escape From Germany

In 1933, the Nazi Party came to power in Germany. They disliked Jews and encouraged violent attacks against them. By 1945, millions of Jews had been murdered by the Nazis. *Escape From Germany* is a novel about a Jewish family who go on the run to escape Nazi violence.

Berlin, 9th November 1938

CRASH!

The sound of shattering glass burst into Margot's dream. She sat up in bed. The curtains were rippling with red light from the street outside. She was scared, but she had to see
5 what was happening.

She tiptoed to the window and looked out. She gasped in horror. Across the road Herr Lowenstein's shop was on fire. Flames roared from the windows, leaping into the darkness and falling back, like tigers on a leash. Further down the street Heimpi's sweet shop was ablaze.

10 Down below people were running, black against the red firelight. Herr and Frau* Lowenstein were out in their night-clothes, desperately throwing buckets of water at the flames. But worst of all a crowd of men stood watching and laughing, throwing stones at them as people fought to save their homes. The men wore armbands with bent crosses on them, swastikas*, and Margot knew they were Nazis, supporters of Adolf Hitler, the German leader.

15 "You bullies!" Margot pounded her fists on the glass. Someone looked up. She realised with a shock that it was Peter, the boy from the next street who only last summer had let her have a ride on his new bike. As she looked down at him in horror, he bent down to pick up a stone. She screamed as he hurled it straight at her.

"Margot! Get away from the window, now!"

20 Papa pulled her away from the window just as the stone smashed through the glass, sending splinters all over the room. He held her close in his arms.

"Oh, Margot, you must not take such risks. They will hurt you!"

Margot was still furious, even though she was shaking with fear.

"But we must stand up to them, Papa! Look what they are doing!"

An extract from
Escape From Germany
by Penny McKinlay.

Glossary
Herr and Frau — Mr and Mrs   swastikas — symbols of the Nazi Party

(1) Why is there "red light" coming through Margot's window (line 4)?

....

1 mark

(2) The author compares the flames to "tigers on a leash" (line 8). Why do you think she chose this comparison?

....

....

2 marks

(3) In your own words, explain why people are "running" (line 10) outside Margot's window.

....

....

1 mark

(4) a. What is different about line 2 compared with the rest of the extract?

....

1 mark

b. Why do you think the author chose to start her book like this?

....

1 mark

(5) How do you think Margot feels when she sees Peter taking part in the violence? Explain your answer.

....

....

2 marks

(6) Explain what this extract tells you about Margot's personality.

....

2 marks

....

Total
out of 10

....

Poems about the Weather

The Wind and Your Dresses both describe different kinds of weather and how they affect people. The Wind was written by Robert Louis Stevenson more than 100 years ago. Your Dresses is a modern poem. It was written by the Scottish poet and playwright Carol Ann Duffy.

The Wind

I saw you toss the kites on high
And blow the birds about the sky;
And all around I heard you pass,
Like ladies' skirts across the grass —
5   O wind, a-blowing all day long,
      O wind, that sings so loud a song!

I saw the different things you did,
But always you yourself you hid.
I felt you push, I heard you call,
10 I could not see yourself at all —
      O wind, a-blowing all day long,
      O wind, that sings so loud a song!

O you that are so strong and cold,
O blower, are you young or old?
15 Are you a beast of field and tree,
Or just a stronger child than me?
      O wind, a-blowing all day long,
      O wind, that sings so loud a song!

Robert Louis Stevenson

Your Dresses

I like your rain dress,
its strange, sad colour,
its small buttons like tears.

I like your fog dress,
5 how it swirls around you
when you dance on the lawn.

Your snow dress I like,
its million snowflakes
sewn together with a needle of ice.

10 But I love your thunderstorm dress,
its huge, dark petticoats,
its silver stitches flashing as you run away.

Carol Ann Duffy

(1) Which poem has a regular rhyming pattern?

....

1 mark

(2) Write down one word that has a similar meaning to "toss" on line 1 of *The Wind*.

....

1 mark

(3) Write down one adjective to describe the wind in lines 7-10 of *The Wind*.
Explain your answer.

....

....

2 marks

(4) What do you think the "small buttons" on line 3 of *Your Dresses* might be?

....

1 mark

(5) Which type of weather does the narrator of *Your Dresses* like best? Explain your answer.

....

....

2 marks

(6) The word "swirls" on line 5 of *Your Dresses* is (circle one):

a. an adverb   b. a preposition   c. a pronoun   d. a verb

1 mark

(7) Which poem do you prefer? Explain your answer.

....

....

Total
out of 10

2 marks

Wayne Rooney: Captain of England

Tom and Matt Oldfield wrote this biography about the English footballer Wayne Rooney in 2015. Rooney began professional football at 16 years old and became an international star. This extract is from the start of the biography and describes Rooney's first match with Manchester United.

'Roo-ney! Roo-ney! Roo-ney!'

It was the sound of 75,000 fans chanting his name. Wayne just stared straight ahead down the tunnel. His heart was beating fast — in fact, it had been pounding since he put on the famous red Manchester United shirt in the dressing room ten minutes earlier. It was a long time
5   since he had felt this nervous playing football. But then this wasn't just any game.

It was 28 September 2004 and he was just minutes away from the start of his United career. Where was the referee? 'Come on, let's go,' he muttered to himself.

That night's game against Turkish giants Fenerbahce in the Champions League was the start of a new chapter for Wayne. He was following in the footsteps of George Best, Bobby
10   Charlton, Eric Cantona, Bryan Robson and so many other United legends. Now Wayne would have the chance to add his name to that list.

As he thought about his whirlwind journey from the streets of Croxteth in Liverpool to the Theatre of Dreams*, he smiled to himself. He had started his first Premier League game for Everton just two years ago and now he was about to make his debut for one of the biggest clubs
15   in the world. The hairs on his neck stood on end.

A broken bone in his foot had delayed his debut and United had begun the season without him. But all anyone wanted to know was when Wayne would be back. When would United fans get their first glimpse of the teenage sensation who had cost £30 million that summer? And how would he top his incredible performances at Euro 2004?

20   Wayne wanted to make up for lost time. His foot had been fine in training this week and he just hoped there would be no pain once he put it to the test in a real game.

As crowds of United fans walked down Sir Matt Busby Way that night, there was a different buzz in the air. Wayne would be making his debut and they were going to share in that experience. Many of them already had 'Rooney' on the back of their United shirts.

25   Just before the teams took to the pitch, Ryan Giggs walked up to Wayne and patted him on the back. Maybe he could sense the newcomer's nerves. 'Don't put too much pressure on yourself tonight. Just enjoy it — you only get to make your Manchester United debut once!'

He winked then shook Wayne's hand. 'The club's going to be in your hands some day soon. This is where it all begins for you.'

Glossary
Theatre of Dreams — nickname for Manchester United's football stadium

An extract from *Wayne Rooney: Captain of England* by Tom and Matt Oldfield.

1 Why have the authors put quotation marks around the text in line 1?

....

1 mark

2 Why do you think this match "wasn't just any game" (line 5)?

....

....

1 mark

3 What does the word "whirlwind" (line 12) mean? What does this word suggest about the way Rooney's career has developed?

....

....

2 marks

4 What do you think the word "debut" (line 14) means? Use a dictionary to help you.

....

1 mark

5 Explain why Rooney was late starting the season.

....

....

1 mark

6 How is the crowd feeling in lines 22-24? How can you tell?

....

....

2 marks

7 Why do you think the authors decided to begin Rooney's biography with this passage?

....

....

2 marks

Total
out of 10

The Lion, the Witch and the Wardrobe

The Lion, the Witch and the Wardrobe is the first book in the *Chronicles of Narnia* series by C.S. Lewis. The story is set in a magical kingdom called Narnia. One day, some children enter Narnia through their wardrobe. In this extract, one of them (Edmund) goes off by himself.

The House was really a small castle. It seemed to be all towers; little towers with long pointed spires on them, sharp as needles. They looked like huge dunces' caps* or sorcerers' caps. And they shone in the moonlight and their long shadows looked strange on the snow. Edmund began to be afraid of the House.

5 But it was too late to think of turning back now. He crossed the river on the ice and walked up to the House. There was nothing stirring; not the slightest sound anywhere. Even his own feet made no noise on the deep newly-fallen snow. He walked on and on, past corner after corner of the House, and past turret* after turret to find the door. He had to go right round to the far side before he found it. It was a huge arch but the great iron gates stood wide open.

10 Edmund crept up to the arch and looked inside into the courtyard, and there he saw a sight that nearly made his heart stop beating. Just inside the gate, with the moonlight shining on it, stood an enormous lion crouched as if it were ready to spring. And Edmund stood in the shadow of the arch, afraid to go on and afraid to go back, with his knees knocking together. He stood there so long that his teeth would have been chattering with cold even if they had not been chattering with fear. How 15 long this really lasted I don't know, but it seemed to Edmund to last for hours.

Then at last he began to wonder why the lion was standing so still — for it hadn't moved one inch since he first set eyes on it. Edmund now ventured a little nearer, still keeping in the shadow of the arch as much as he could. He now saw 20 from the way the lion was standing that it couldn't have been looking at him at all. ("But supposing it turns its head?" thought Edmund.) In fact it was staring at something else — namely a little dwarf who stood with its back to it about four feet away. "Aha!" thought Edmund. "When it springs at the 25 dwarf then will be my chance to escape." But still the lion never moved, nor did the dwarf. And now at last Edmund remembered what the others had said about the White Witch turning people into stone. Perhaps this was only a stone lion. And as soon as he had thought of that he noticed that the lion's back and the top of its head were covered with snow. Of course 30 it must only be a statue! No living animal would have let itself get covered with snow. Then very slowly and with his heart beating as if it would burst, Edmund ventured to go up to the lion. Even now he hardly dared touch it, but at last he put out his hand, very quickly, and did.

An extract from *The Lion, the Witch and the Wardrobe* by C.S. Lewis.

Glossary	
dunces' cap — a tall pointy hat	turret — a small tower often built on the corner of a building

1 The author says that the House's towers were as "sharp as needles" (line 2). Do you think this makes it seem like a nice place? Explain your answer.

....

....

2 marks

2 What do you notice about the words "on", "corner" and "turret" on lines 7 and 8? Why do you think the author did this?

....

....

2 marks

3 The word "knocking" on line 13 is (circle one):

a. a verb   b. an adverb   c. an adjective   d. a noun

1 mark

4 What season is it in this extract? How can you tell?

....

....

2 marks

5 The author says that Edmund's heart was "beating as if it would burst" (line 31). Why do you think he chose this phrase?

....

....

1 mark

6 Would you like to meet the White Witch? Explain your answer.

....

....

2 marks

....

Total
out of 10

Year 4 — Targeted Comprehension

A Letter from Barack Obama

Barack Obama was the President of the United States of America between 2009-2017. When he was elected, he wrote a letter to his daughters, Malia and Sasha, who were aged 11 and 8 at the time. The following extract from his letter explains why he decided to run for president.

Dear Malia and Sasha,

[...]

When I was a young man, I thought life was all about me — about how I'd make my way in the world, become successful, and get the things I want. But then the two of you came into my world with all your curiosity and mischief and those smiles that never fail to fill my heart and light up my

5   day. And suddenly, all my big plans for myself didn't seem so important anymore. I soon found that the greatest joy in my life was the joy I saw in yours. And I realized that my own life wouldn't count for much unless I was able to ensure that you had every opportunity for happiness and fulfillment in yours. In the end, girls, that's why I ran for President: because of what I want for you and for every child in this nation.

10   I want all our children to go to schools worthy of their potential — schools that challenge them, inspire them, and instill in them a sense of wonder about the world around them. I want them to have the chance to go to college — even if their parents aren't rich. And I want them to get good jobs: jobs that pay well and give them benefits like health care, jobs that let them spend time with their own kids and retire with dignity.

15   I want us to push the boundaries of discovery so that you'll live to see new technologies and inventions that improve our lives and make our planet cleaner and safer. And I want us to push our own human boundaries to reach beyond the divides of race and region, gender and religion that keep us from seeing the best in each other.

[...]

These are the things I want for you — to grow up in a world with no limits on your dreams and
20   no achievements beyond your reach, and to grow into compassionate, committed women who will help build that world. And I want every child to have the same chances to learn and dream and grow and thrive that you girls have. That's why I've taken our family on this great adventure.

I am so proud of both of you. I love you more than you can ever know. And I am grateful every day for your patience, poise, grace, and humor as we prepare to start our new life together in the
25   White House.

Love, Dad

1 How did having children change Barack's outlook on life?

....

1 mark

2 Barack says children should go to schools that are "worthy of their potential" (line 10). What do you think he means by this?

....

....

1 mark

3 Does Barack think that a good job gives you a better lifestyle? Explain your answer.

....

....

2 marks

4 According to Barack, what stops people from "seeing the best in each other" (line 18)?

....

1 mark

5 What is the "great adventure" (line 22) that Barack refers to?

....

1 mark

6 Explain what this letter tells you about Barack's personality.

....

....

2 marks

7 What do you think your life would be like if one of your family members was the President of the USA? Explain your answer.

....

2 marks

....

Total
out of 10

....

The Jungle Book

The Jungle Book is a collection of stories by the British author Rudyard Kipling. Published in 1893-4, they tell the tale of a human boy called Mowgli who is raised by a pack of wolves in an Indian jungle. In this extract, Mowgli has fled from the jungle and arrives at a village.

When Mowgli left the wolf's cave after the fight with the Pack at the Council Rock, he went down to the plowed lands where the villagers lived, but he would not stop there because it was too near the jungle, and he knew that he had made

5 at least one bad enemy at the Council. So he hurried on, keeping to the rough road that ran down the valley, and followed it at a steady jog-trot for nearly twenty miles, till he came to a country that he did not know. The valley opened out into a great plain dotted over with rocks and cut up by ravines*. At one end stood a little village, and at the other the thick jungle came down in a sweep to the grazing–grounds, and

10 stopped there as though it had been cut off with a hoe. All over the plain, cattle and buffaloes were grazing, and when the little boys in charge of the herds saw Mowgli they shouted and ran away, and the yellow pariah* dogs that hang about every Indian village barked. Mowgli walked on, for he was feeling hungry, and when he came to the village gate he saw the big thorn-bush that was drawn up before the gate at twilight, pushed to one side.

15 "Umph!" he said, for he had come across more than one such barricade in his night rambles after things to eat. "So men are afraid of the People of the Jungle here also." He sat down by the gate, and when a man came out he stood up, opened his mouth, and pointed down it to show that he wanted food. The man stared, and ran back up the one street of the village shouting for the priest, who was a big, fat man dressed in white, with a red and yellow

20 mark on his forehead. The priest came to the gate, and with him at least a hundred people, who stared and talked and shouted and pointed at Mowgli.

"They have no manners, these Men Folk," said Mowgli to himself. "Only the gray ape would behave as they do." So he threw back his long hair and frowned at the crowd.

"What is there to be afraid of?" said the priest. "Look at the marks on his arms and legs.

25 They are the bites of wolves. He is but a wolf-child run away from the jungle."

Of course, in playing together, the cubs had often nipped Mowgli harder than they intended, and there were white scars all over his arms and legs. But he would have been the last person in the world to call these bites; for he knew what real biting meant.

"Arre! Arre!" said two or three women together. "To be bitten by wolves, poor child!

30 He is a handsome boy. He has eyes like red fire. By my honor, Messua, he is not unlike thy boy that was taken by the tiger."

An extract from *The Jungle Book* by Rudyard Kipling.

Glossary	
ravine — a steep and narrow valley	pariah — stray

1 Why has Mowgli fled from the jungle?

....

....

1 mark

2 How do you think the little boys feel when they
see Mowgli (lines 11-12)? Explain your answer.

....

....

2 marks

3 What does the word "barricade" (line 15) mean? Use a dictionary to help you.

....

1 mark

4 Why do you think Mowgli points to his open mouth instead of asking directly for food?

....

....

2 marks

5 Explain how the villagers' reaction to Mowgli
changes from line 18 to the end of the extract.

....

....

2 marks

6 Did this extract make you want to read the rest of the book? Explain your answer.

....

2 marks

....

....

Total
out of 10

An Unexpected Visitor

By now, you've had plenty of practice at reading texts and answering questions. Now it's time to write your own text, think of some questions and then swap with a friend.

Imagine a dinosaur has been spotted close to your house. Write a story about how people around you react and what you decide to do. We've made a start, but what happens next is up to you!

Mum was calling me from the kitchen, but I didn't respond. I was rooted to the spot, staring at our television screen. A shaky video was showing a dinosaur, a REAL dinosaur, slowly lumbering down a street, past a school. My school.

E4CW221